Tips for Reading Together

Children learn best when reading is fun.

- Talk about the title and the pictures on the cover.
- Discuss what you think the story might be about.
- Read the story together, inviting your child to read as much of it as they can.
- Give lots of praise as your child reads, and help them when necessary.
- Try different ways of helping if they get stuck on a word. For example, get them to say the first sound of the word, or break it into chunks, or read the whole sentence again, trying to guess the word. Focus on the meaning.
- Have fun finding the desert rat and the letters and letter shapes hidden in the pictures.
- Re-read the story later, encouraging your child to read as much of it as they can.

Children enjoy re-reading stories and this helps to build their confidence.

Have fun!

Find the letters and letter shapes hidden in the pictures that spell out the word TREASURE, and look for the desert rat.

The Secret of the Sands

Written by Cynthia Rider

Illustrated by Alex Brychta

OXFORD

UNIVERSITY PRESS

The children were playing on the computer. They were playing Chip's new game, Secret of the Sands.

Suddenly, the magic key began to glow. "Look at the key!" cried Biff. "It's time for an adventure."

Floppy growled. He didn't want an
adventure, but the magic was
starting to work.

The magic took the children into
a desert. They saw a boy riding a
camel across the hot sands.

8

The boy rode up to them.

"My name is Ali," he said. "You must come to my tent. You can't stay out in this hot sun."

Ali helped the children climb onto the camels. Floppy sat with Kipper.

"This camel is too bumpy for me," thought Floppy.

Ali took the children to his tent.
He gave them some cooler clothes.
Then he showed them a map.

"I'm going to the village on this map," said Ali. "Nobody lives there now, but long ago my father hid some treasure there. He called it the Secret of the Sands."

"Secret of the Sands! That's the
same name as my game," cried
Chip. "Can we help you to find the
treasure?"

"Oh yes! I'd like you to help," said
Ali. "Come on, let's go!"

They rode through deep, rocky
valleys and up steep, sandy hills.

At last, they came to the village. There was sand everywhere. It had blown into the empty rooms and drifted over the walls.

"There must have been a
sandstorm," said Ali. "It all looks
different from the map. I don't know
where to look."

Wilf pointed to an old tower.
"That's the tower on the map," he said. "We must be very near the treasure. Let's look here."

They looked into the shadowy
rooms and poked the sand with sticks.
"I'll help, too," thought Floppy,
and he dug some deep holes.

Suddenly, Floppy disappeared.
"Help!" shouted Biff. "Floppy has
fallen down a hole. We must rescue
him."

They climbed down into a hidden room. Wilma shone her torch around and something glittered in the light. It was a treasure chest!

The chest was full of glittering
gold and sparkling jewels.

"The Secret of the Sands!" said Ali.
"How beautiful!"

The children put the chest onto
Ali's camel.

Suddenly, they heard a noise. It
grew louder and louder.

Two men on a motorbike came speeding towards them.

"They're desert robbers," cried Ali. "They're after the treasure!"

The children raced away but the robbers came closer and closer. "They're going to catch us," cried Biff. "What can we do?"

Suddenly, there was a loud crash!
"Floppy has saved us!" shouted
Kipper. "The robbers have fallen
into one of his holes. They'll never
get us now."

They got back safely, and Ali gave
Floppy a golden camel. "Thank you
for saving us," he said.

The magic key began to glow.

"It's time for us to go," said Biff.

The magic took the children
home.

"What an adventure!" said Chip.

"What glittering gold!" said Wilma.

"What big bumpy camels!"
thought Floppy.

Why do you think the book is called The Secret of the Sands?

Why didn't Floppy like the adventure?

How did Floppy save the children?

What sort of treasure would you like to find?

A maze

Help Ali find the treasure.

Useful common words repeated in this story and other books in the series. began children cried down gave louder now shouted some suddenly they're thought were what with

Names in this story: Ali Biff Chip Kipper Wilf Wilma Floppy

More books for you to enjoy

Level 1: Getting Ready

Level 2: Starting to Read

Level 3: Becoming a Reader

Level 4: Building Confidence

Level 5: Reading with Confidence

OXFORD
UNIVERSITY PRESS

Great Clarendon Street,
Oxford OX2 6DP

Text © Cynthia Rider 2006
Illustrations © Alex Brychta 2006
This edition published 2010

First published 2006
All rights reserved

Read at Home Series Editors:
Kate Ruttle, Annemarie Young

British Library Cataloguing
in Publication Data available

ISBN: 9780198387695

10 9 8 7 6 5 4 3 2 1

Printed in China by Imago

Have more fun with Read at Home